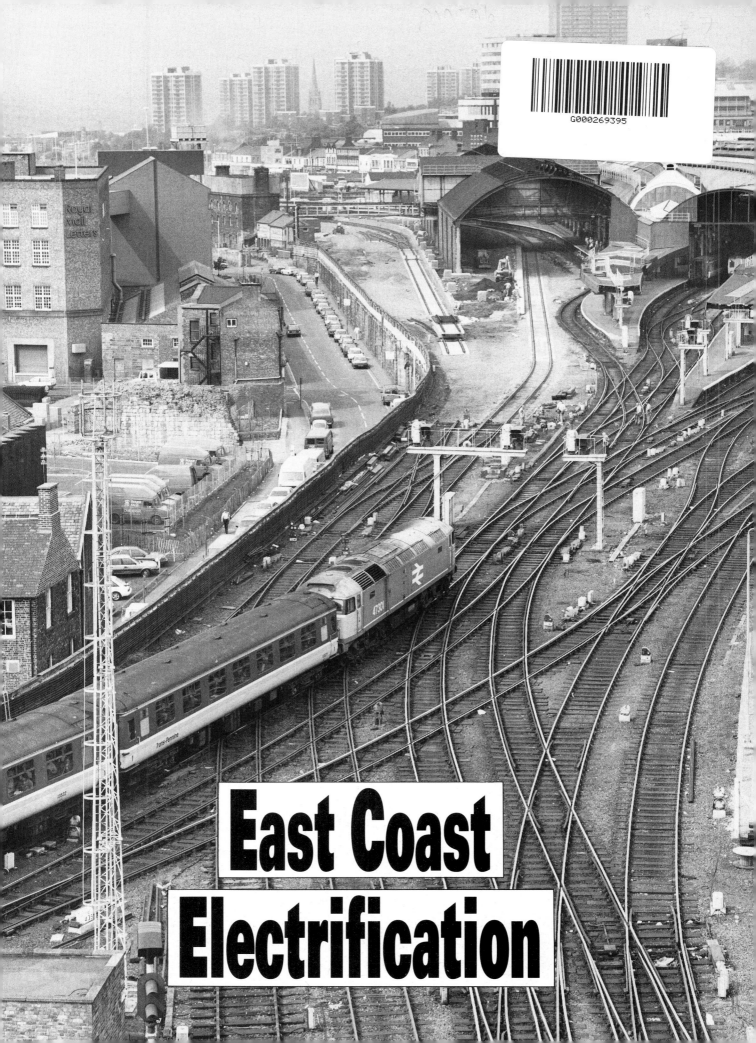

East Coast
Electrification

East Coast

Electrification

COLIN BOOCOCK

LONDON

IAN ALLAN LTD

Contents

First published 1991

ISBN 0 7110 1979 7

Published by Ian Allan Ltd, Shepperton, Surrey; and printed by Ian Allan Printing Ltd at their works at Coombelands in Runnymede, England

Acknowledgements

The East Coast main line electrification project has been a major undertaking. Many people within and outside British Rail who had a role to play in the project's success worked long hours in ensuring its timely and fruitful completion. I am therefore very grateful that so many colleagues and friends were willing to find time to advise me on project details, and to read through and correct the draft manuscript.

Helpers have been too numerous for me to name here. Let it suffice therefore that any person who reads this book in the knowledge that he or she has helped in its preparation receives here and now my public thanks.

Colin Boocock

Above:
This flashback to former years when East Coast main line trains had Mk 2 stock and Class 47 or 55 diesel locomotives shows No 47518 leaving Berwick with an Edinburgh-bound InterCity train. *Dr L. A. Nixon*

Front cover:
On 18 March 1990 Class 91 locomotive No 91006 heads a rake of new Mk 4 coaches on the Sunday 09.15 King's Cross to Leeds near South Elmsall, north of Doncaster. *Peter J. Robinson*

Rear cover:
A DVT leads an up Leeds-King's Cross service through Grantham on 31 May 1990. *David Sparkes*

First Title Page
Work had already started on the new platform alignments on the east side of Newcastle station when this photograph was taken on 23 May 1989. Diesel No 47301 approaches from the Gateshead direction with a Trans-Pennine train from Liverpool Lime Street. *Dr W. A. Sharman*

Main title page (double page spread)
No 91001 stands at the rear of the 16.10 from Leeds to King's Cross at Peterborough on 9 August 1989. This was during the month when most Leeds trains began to be worked by Class 91 locomotives. They were used in push-pull mode on trains of IC125-type Mk 3 coaches using converted InterCity 125 power cars as surrogate driving trailers. *Colin Boocock*

1.
The Project

The electrification of the East Coast main line of British Rail has attracted many superlatives. It has been called 'Britain's longest construction site'. The Class 91 locomotives which have been supplied for the route are hailed as 'the most powerful locomotives ever to work in Britain'. One of them now holds Britain's rail speed record for locomotives. Much has been made of the ever-reducing cost of electrifying a main line railway, and of the detailed attention to East Coast main line (ECML) environmental design.

None of this however uncovers the full excitement or complexity of the project. Compared with the electrification schemes undertaken in Britain in the 1950s and 1960s the ECML scheme has been quite different in its execution and its successful implementation. It did not cause widespread disruption to everyday passenger traffic. According to project director Don Heath, the project has run to time throughout, and has kept within its budget. Indeed the announcement that electric trains would run from King's Cross to Leeds *a year earlier than originally planned* was a striking illustration of the ability of modern planning and project management methods to deliver in excess of what was promised.

This *Modern Railways Special* describes the project in some detail, and takes the reader through the processes which ensured its success.

The case for electrifying to Leeds, Newcastle and Edinburgh was actually a very complex one to develop. The government of the day required that all large capital schemes should make a return on investment of at least 7% of the capital employed. British Rail had set up the five business Sectors, of which InterCity was the prime user of the East Coast main line. InterCity Director Cyril Bleasdale therefore took the lead in preparing the case for electrification. Various parts of the case went through many changes as the details were developed, discussed and the many different alternatives compared and evaluated. The government, and indeed the Board's own investment

analysts, would expect to see that every reasonable option had been considered carefully before the key decisions were taken that would enable the final project to be evolved. This was necessary despite the fact that the money to be spent was BR's own.

As an example of the debates which ensued, there was much discussion about which routes should be put 'under the wire'. How many tracks on these routes should be wired? What about loops, yards and sidings? Wiring under-utilised sections might not be justified, unless it caused disproportionate expense in provision of alternative (diesel) traction.

Why indeed was it now considered to be the right time to discuss electrifying this railway?

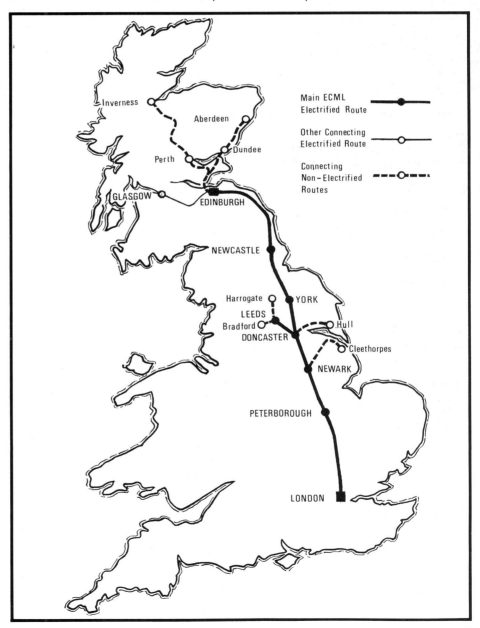

Right:
ECML electrified route.

There is actually a clear, definitive answer to the last question. InterCity was facing the need to consider the future of the High Speed Train sets (IC125 or 'HST' in general parlance) in view of the escalating costs at that time of keeping the powercars running. The ECML timetable was a punishing one for the IC125s to follow, with very high mileages being run each working day.

InterCity also had a wish to eliminate non-air-conditioned coaching stock from its regular services. The possibility of cascading IC125 sets to less heavily pressed routes was also a useful option to consider.

However, the requirement to meet a 7% return on capital did not at first seem to provide the wherewithal to do more than replace the diesel powercars with electric locomotives, and an early option included the potential reuse of the carriages from the existing High Speed Trains.

There was nonetheless no doubt that one modern, powerful electric locomotive was financially a good replacement for two diesel powercars. But nagging questions required resolution of a number of options for the trains themselves:

● Was it sensible to rely on using the existing Mk 3 IC125 carriages? Would that not negate the remaining useful lives of the displaced diesel powercars?
● How should the through workings to places like Bradford and Harrogate be handled?
● Should there continue to be through workings to Dundee, Aberdeen and Inverness? If so, what traction should be used north of Edinburgh?

The debate went on for many months at Board HQ and among the Regions involved (Eastern and Scottish). The solution to the Bradford and Harrogate extension was to emerge after the basic type of train set had been determined. The Scottish question was much more difficult.

The idea that passengers would have to change trains in Edinburgh, after through running had been available for over a century, was anathema to InterCity's route managers as well as ScotRail's General Manager at the time, Chris Green. The inconvenience to customers was not considered accept-

able, and the extra time needed to make guaranteed connections would risk the imposition of a longer journey time from London after electrification than before. The journey time from Edinburgh to Aberdeen would in any case be extended because of:

● the need to change traction, and
● the use of diesel locomotives which were not allowed to curve through Fife as fast as the lighter IC125 powercars were.

An alternative proposal that the trains north of Edinburgh should be hauled by pairs of otherwise redundant IC125 powercars marshalled back-to-back was canvassed but not progressed.

The dilemma over through trains beyond Edinburgh was eased by the very substantial time reductions made possible south of Edinburgh as a result of the high power performance of the new Class 91 locomotives and the track and signalling improvements. Thus, an engine change or a change of train at Edinburgh ceased to be the emotive problem it otherwise would have been. (As it turned out, neither solution was adopted, as seen in Chapter 9.)

Early thoughts on traction for the ECML electrification had centred on the use of powerful Co-Co locomotives capable of 125mph running and suitable for both the West and East Coast main lines. Thus a contract was let to Brush of Loughborough to build a prototype locomotive, and the Class 89 was the result. Railway business aspirations, however, developed further while the prototype was under construction. InterCity foresaw a market need for its ECML locomotives to run at 140mph well before their half life, and the specification was expanded to include the need to haul freight and parcels trains as well as day and night InterCity trains.

Thus the Class 91, when it emerged from BREL Crewe under subcontract from GEC, was altogether a revolutionary machine. Chapter 5 tells why. By this time InterCity had also established its policy for push-pull operation of its electric locomotive-powered trains. This had as its main objective the avoidance of useful locomotives and train crews standing at bufferstops at terminus station turnrounds, but also

produced many other advantages, chief among which were:

● It enabled locomotives to be dedicated to InterCity workings.

● This would lead to maintenance being tailored to that sector's own requirements, and that the locomotives could be maintained in sequence with (and coupled to) their train sets.

● Keeping the locomotives attached to their trains for as long as possible would reduce the damage to couplings and jumper connections which is common in normal operations involving replacing locomotives at turnround.

The need eventually to run at 140mph confirmed the decision to purchase new coaching stock for the ECML to coincide with the electrification. Thus was born the concept of the Mk 4 carriage which is described in some detail in Chapter 5. A train set would consist of a Class 91 locomotive at the north end, followed by eight Mk 4 coaches and trailed by a streamlined driving van trailer. Enough power was to be installed in the Class 91 to enable longer trains to be moved at high speeds, and indeed the newly built trains are already planned to be extended to nine cars. The design, production and commissioning of the new trains was the responsibility of the InterCity 225 Project Director, David Rollin, with Andrew Higton as Project Engineer.

Having settled the question of what the InterCity train configuration was to be, it became apparent that the answer to Bradford's and Harrogate's problem was simply to diesel-haul the whole train set, including the dead electric locomotive, beyond Leeds. This was no worse than wasting locomotive time on run-round, and it enabled the policy of keeping train and locomotive together to be sustained. It also significantly simplified the coupling and uncoupling to be done at Leeds, compared with a traditional locomotive change.

Proving the case financially was done by using the discounted cash flow technique. In this technique, the earnings and expenditure for each year of the full lives of the principal assets of the project are estimated. For years that run into the future the figures are reduced by an agreed percentage for each year — the test discount rate, which was 7% on BR at the time of the ECML financial appraisal. Thus the events which are expected to take place many years from now have less influence on the financial case than years in the

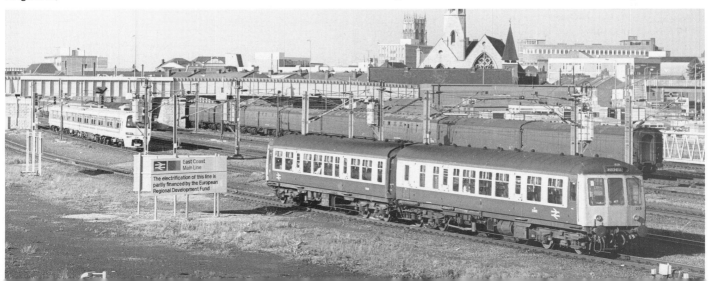

Right:
Erection of the overhead catenary and contact wires from the roof of a wiring train has to be carried out in all weathers to a tight time schedule. This team happily has a dry night in which to work near Leeds. *British Rail*

Centre right:
Where possible, every consideration is given to the environmental effects of works associated with electrification. This old stone overbridge has its new span supported by concrete arch sections and yet has not lost its traditional style. *British Rail*

Bottom right:
The culmination of the first main stage of the project was the introduction of full InterCity 225 working between Leeds and London in January 1990. This train of Mk 4 stock led by a driving van trailer is propelled by No 91009 and forms the 11.10 from Leeds. It is approaching Peterborough at speed on 16 February 1990. *Dr W. A. Sharman*

immediate future. The annual net cash flows are added together at their discounted values, to produce a figure known as the net present value of the project. The option with the best net present value is likely to be selected as the best option, all other important variables being equal. In the case of the ECML electrification, the best option by a clear margin was the one chosen.

Designing the overhead wire system, the preparations for construction, and the effort put in to ensure the wiring work did not affect day-to-day running, are all described in Chapter 4. All this was achieved at a record low cost per mile in real terms, and considerably more quickly than had originally been anticipated.

Other background work such as immunising the signalling systems and setting up modern electronic signal control is the subject of Chapter 8, while Chapter 7 covers the considerable civil engineering programme. A total of 157 bridges had to be raised or rebuilt, tracks slewed or lowered, and nine station layouts realigned and simplified to suit modern conditions. While some of these schemes would have been implemented in any case at some time or other, their implementation simultaneously with the main electrification project enabled the greatest benefits to be obtained.

The impact which the East Coast main line electrification will have on InterCity business on the route will surely be substantial because so many smaller sub-projects have been enacted together. The difficult challenge of producing something better than the IC125s) has been met successfully. The 'nose-cone effect' (the upsurge in traffic generated by the striking image of the IC125s) has been upstaged by the potential for a real 'sparks effect' when electric trains begin working to and from Edinburgh.

As is often said in management textbooks when it comes to defining *synergy*: 'The whole is greater than the sum of the parts.'

2.
Past Perfections

History tells us about the races to the north in the 'golden era' of railways in Victorian times. Energetic competition between the railway companies which linked together to offer fast trains from London to Aberdeen had consolidated on to two key routes:

● King's Cross to Aberdeen via York, Newcastle, Edinburgh and Dundee, offered by the Great Northern, the North Eastern and the North British Railways; and
● Euston to Aberdeen via Preston, Carlisle, Motherwell and Perth, operated by the London & North Western and the Caledonian Railways.

The East Coast route timing in 1887 was 9hr for the King's Cross to Edinburgh trains. At the end of the 1888 races this was reduced to 8¼hr. The 1895 races picked up the overall timings to Aberdeen, and on this occasion the West Coast route was said to be superior, though it is unclear how much of that was due to the influence of the signalman at Kinnaber Junction where the Caledonian and North British lines joined up before the last stage of the northbound run.

The '1888 agreement' time of 8¼hr for the London-Edinburgh run was adhered to right through until 1932. Nonetheless competition continued, and the process whereby the East Coast route would be fastest for a period only

to be overtaken by the West Coast route with a new, faster timetable, developed as the 20th century progressed. Normally this 'leap-frogging' has taken place in more competitive times, such as in the 1930s when the London, Midland & Scottish Railway (LMS) beat the LNER time from London to Edinburgh when the LMS streamlined express, the 'Coronation Scot' began running from Euston to Glasgow. The LNER answered with the 'A4' Pacifics and streamlined trains like the 'Silver Jubilee' and the 'Coronation', the latter being timed at a record 6hr from King's Cross to Edinburgh. (At that time, ordinary trains were scheduled to reach Edinburgh in 7hr.) The LMS then claimed a world speed record when a Stanier 4-6-2 reached 114mph on the approach to Crewe, only to be pipped by Sir Nigel Gresley's *Mallard* with 126mph descending Stoke bank in 1938.

Then came World War 2, times of austerity, and a general speed limit of 60mph on British main line railways. We had to wait until the early 1950s before things got moving again — but then they did! It is difficult to recall the order in which things happened at that time, but clearly the introduction of the West Coast 'Caledonian' fast train from Glasgow to London was an attempt, particularly when one recalls the *Daily Express* claiming a scoop when it photographed from the air a blue 'Duchess' at speed on the very day when British Railways claimed that the train had beaten the record for the Glasgow-London run. The Eastern, North Eastern and Scottish Regions'

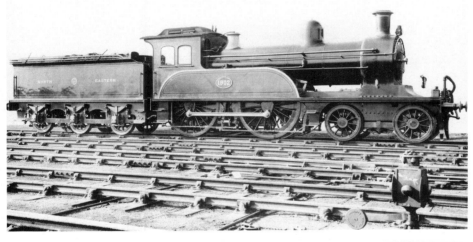

Above left:
The 19th century 'races to the North' utilised the best express passenger locomotives of the participating companies. In the 1895 races the North Eastern Railway used large-wheeled 4-4-0s, similar to No 1902 shown here, for the Doncaster to Newcastle stretch.
Courtesy National Railway Museum

Left:
Typical of Great Northern Railway ECML trains in the early years of the 20th century was this formation, photographed north of Peterborough with Ivatt 'small Atlantic' 4-4-2 No 989 at the head.
C. Laundy courtesy National Railway Museum

'Elizabethan' train which ran nonstop between King's Cross and Edinburgh, however, was for most of the BR steam era timetabled faster than the 'Caledonian'. Neither, however, attained the exemplary timings of the prewar streamliners.

It must be emphasised that these steam flyers were lightweight formations of around seven or eight coaches hauled by the best top link locomotives. They did not represent the normal speeds or timings of other express trains on these routes, which were considerably more pedestrian.

The introduction of diesel electric locomotives on the West Coast and East Coast routes initially did little to enhance long distance journey times. Locomotives of only 2,000hp, as were the English Electric Type 4s, could run no harder than a 'Duchess' or 'A4'. Even though the diesels had a much higher starting performance, they could hardly match, let alone beat, everyday steam '8P' running. The advent of the 2,500hp 'Peak' class 1Co-Co1s increased the scope for improvement, but their 90mph top speed fell short of what was really needed.

Successful modernisation of the two routes had to wait several years. Meanwhile in 1955 the English Electric Co had offered its prototype 3,300hp 'Deltic' Co-Co for testing. The locomotive spent a few years on both the West and East Coast routes. Its potential was perhaps wasted on trains like the 'Manxman' from Liverpool Lime Street to Euston, but its potential to run consistently at 100mph *did* register on Eastern Region management.

As a clear exception to the normal run of BR diesel policy, 22 production 'Deltics' were purchased. The case made for their purchase rested on the claim that, given high utilisation, the 22 diesels would replace 55 Pacific steam locomotives.

The 'Deltic' fleet entered traffic in 1961 and revolutionised train running on the East Coast main line. Consistent 100mph running was now possible on most daily express trains, putting high speed running at the disposal of the general public, not just the few who in years past had afforded the supplementary fares of the streamliners. The East

Coast route was now much faster to Scotland than the West Coast line, with timings equivalent to the old 'Coronation' speeds.

Electrification of the West Coast route first linked Crewe with Manchester and then Liverpool. It was later extended to Euston. In 1974 the line north from Weaver Junction was electrified to Motherwell where it met the Glasgow area electrification scheme end-on. At 25kV it represented the 'state of the art' in modern ac overhead systems, even though the latest 5,000hp Class 87 Bo-Bo locomotives were conventional machines using tap-changers for voltage control.

Such traction power enabled drastic schedule improvements to be made between London Euston and Glasgow Central. The 'Royal Scot' was timed at 5hr end-to-end, other trains averaging

around 5½hr with more stops. Clearly a challenge had arrived for the East Coast 'Deltics'.

The situation was reversed again as the 1970s closed. The East Coast gained the ascendancy, but not because of any major accelerations. The policy adopted by the Eastern Region (which now embraced the whole route from King's Cross to the Scottish border) was to make simple but significant improvements to track alignments, each small in effect but cumulatively enabling useful journey time reductions. This all happened while the London Midland Region was adding stops and coaches to the 'Royal Scot'. This important train was covering the Glasgow-London run in an extended time of 5½hr by the early 1980s, and losing out to air traffic, as well as to the newest trains which the ECML was by then running.

Above right:
The Gresley Pacifics introduced the era of fast trains and also undertook heavy haulage during World War 2. In this view, No 4470 Great Northern has about 17 coaches behind its tender.
R. F. Dearden courtesy National Railway Museum

Right:
100mph running became the norm for the LNER's streamlined express trains, such as the 'Coronation' seen here passing Ganwick at speed with A4 4-6-2 No 4489 Dominion of Canada at its head.
F. R. Hebron Rail Archive Stephenson

It has been said that the high speed diesel train rescued InterCity (and with it BR) from a continuing downward spiral of traffic and credibility. It certainly was a winner. Marketed as the Inter-City 125, its restyled and highly attractive streamlined front end gave the train not only a powerful 'face' but an extremely friendly one as well. When deployed on the East Coast main line from 1978 the IC125s, with their 125mph balancing speed, broke records in several camps. The prototype IC125 set broke the world speed record for diesel traction when it achieved 143mph during early test runs. (The record was previously held by the prewar German *Fliegender Hamburger*.) Timings from London to Edinburgh came down to 4hr 34min on the fastest trains, almost an hour faster than the best on the electrified WCML.

The IC125s were so popular with customers that overcrowding, previously thought to be a phenomenon which disappeared at the end of the war, became common. Passengers who have had to stand from Doncaster to King's Cross will bear testimony to that. But what a splendid new problem for the railway to have to tackle!

Top:
New steam locomotives delivered in early British Railways days included the Peppercorn Class A1 4-6-2s. No 60159 *Bonnie Dundee* heads the southbound 'Heart of Midlothian' at Newcastle on 27 August 1954. *Brian Morrison*

Left:
Heavyweight diesel electric traction was the order of the day as attempts were made to oust steam traction from its supreme position on the ECML, though without complete success until the 'Deltics' and Class 47s arrived. On 15 April 1960 English Electric Type 4 1Co-Co1 No D209 approaches Hadley Wood with the 12.20 Hull-King's Cross. The train includes a mixture of BR Mk 1 stock and former LNER Gresley and Thompson vehicles. *Colin Boocock*

The solution to the early overcrowding on IC125s was to increase the number of trains in the timetable, including for a while the retention of diesel locomotive-hauled trains. Edinburgh gained an hourly interval service to London — surely the only such frequency over an equivalent distance anywhere in Europe at the time. York received semi-fast trains every hour. In later timetable improvements, Newcastle was also to be served by frequent London trains, independent from the Scottish ones. The Leeds service became roughly hourly, too. The remaining locomotive-hauled InterCity trains were replaced by IC125s as a result of changed InterCity business priorities which enabled the transfer of under-utilised sets from the Western Region.

Then came the economic boom years of the late 1980s, overcrowding did not disappear, and the call came to electrify the East Coast main line. The superiority of train speeds on the East Coast over the West Coast route now seemed set to remain for the foreseeable future.

Over the years the pattern and content of freight train operations on the ECML have also changed dramatically, probably more substantially even

Top:
By 1974 the Cravens-built Pullman cars on the 'Tees-Tyne Pullman' had been liveried in British Rail's corporate identity grey-and-blue style. The train is seen leaving Darlington on 13 June behind 'Deltic' No 55011 *The Royal Northumberland Fusiliers.* *Brian Morrison*

Right:
The Class 55 'Deltics' remained supreme on ECML InterCity trains until the arrival of the '125' sets. No 55002 *The King's Own Yorkshire Light Infantry* drifts downhill past Penmanshiel with a northbound Anglo-Scottish express.
Peter J. Robinson

than the passenger market. In the early BR years, steam-hauled freight trains followed much the same workings as they had for decades previously. There were coal trains from the north for the capital. Fast fish trains, booked to work at 75mph speeds, came south every night from Aberdeen. Trainloads of steel were to be seen on the main line at places such as Darlington and Doncaster. There was also much activity in the hills above Grantham where stone trains were frequently to be seen with Gresley Class O2 2-8-0s at the head. There was mixed freight aplenty, as the ECML was in the forefront of fully braked fast block freight workings. The BR Standard '9F' 2-10-0s shared these duties with former LNER 'V2' 2-6-2s and 'A2' Pacifics. Many of these trains had their steam locomotives replaced by diesels of Classes 31, 37 or 47 in more recent years.

All this has changed. In recent years most freight workings from London to the north have been transferred to the electrified WCML and many Freightliner container trains have left the ECML. What freight there is, heads for the North London connection to the North Thames industrial area or the Anglian ports. There is however much coal transported around the Yorkshire area and in the northeast, in trains of standard HAA merry-go-round (mgr) wagons. Several of the largest power stations are just off the ECML, and Class 56 and 58 diesels are seen in what appears to be an almost endless procession of coal trains passing through Doncaster most weekdays.

What scope is there for electric working of freight trains after ECML electrification? Certainly an order for 21 Class 90 Bo-Bos, the thyristor-controlled version of the trusted Class 87 of the WCML, has been delivered, for freight and parcels workings, a fleet enlargement spurred on by the developments on the East Coast and North London routes. These locomotives are expected to find employment on Freightliner and other freight trains throughout the BR 25kV electrified core network.

The mgr coal trains and the steel trains of the north and northeast will remain diesel hauled because all of them run on non-electrified routes for most of their working day.

There is also little scope for much local passenger traffic to be handled electrically. At the southern end, Network SouthEast services have been extended from Hitchin to terminate at Peterborough, using Class 317 EMUs for the most part. In the middle, as in the Northeast, local services are in the hands of DMUs which begin and end most of their journeys at points quite distant from electrified railways. The West Yorkshire Passenger Transport Executive has been using four-car electric multiple-units for Leeds to Doncaster services from autumn 1990, but this is about as far as the Provincial Sector's involvement in ECML electrification goes, unless the feasibility studies into north Trans-Pennine electrification produce positive results.

Clearly therefore, the dominance of InterCity on the East Coast main line is proven, and it is InterCity which will gain most from the project.

Left:
Modern freight trains to and from the East Anglian and Thames ports, will be able to be electrically hauled along the East Coast main line. This Speedlink train heading south through Peterborough behind No 47008 on 14 June 1984 includes four continental ferry wagons in its consist. *Dr W. A. Sharman*

Below:
The InterCity 125 sets, or 'High Speed Trains' ('HSTs' as they are colloquially known among railwaymen), raised passenger carryings on the East Coast main line to a level requiring more than one train per hour between Edinburgh and London! This set is beginning the southbound climb towards Grantshouse, Scottish Region, on an afternoon working from Edinburgh.
Dr L. A. Nixon

3.
Planning the Project

A project as large as electrifying the East Coast main line is by nature complex. There is so much for which to plan ahead, and so much which impacts on other activities on the railway, as well as other activities within the project itself. Just to explain one aspect of this planning, one should imagine just how many railway and other organisations can be involved in a project such as this:

- The Railways Board
- The Government
- The Eastern Region
- ScotRail
- The Mechanical & Electrical Engineering Department
- The Signal & Telecommunications Department
- The Civil Engineering Department
- The Operations Department
- The Director of Finance
- The Board's Solicitor

- Bodies concerned with protection of the environment
- Local authorities
- British Rail Engineering (now BREL)
- GEC Transportation Projects
- Metro-Cammell
- Balfour Beatty Power Construction
- Pirelli Construction Co
- A host of other suppliers and interested parties.

The list is only for an example. It is very far from complete because a full list of organisations, groups and companies with an interest in the scheme would make very long and tedious reading. What it does show is that there is a large number of interlinking relationships which have to be maintained. One may ask how on earth can the project director co-ordinate them all over such a long timescale and in so many fields of activity.

Several techniques are employed by BR, and indeed most other large bodies, when running a project such as this. A key planning tool is the use of network analysis, or critical path anlaysis as it is often called. This technique is actually quite simple to set up even though the diagrams used within it often appear to be enormously complex.

To lay out a network diagram the planner draws a horizontal line for every activity. The end of each line is linked to the next activity, defined as an activity (there may be more than one) which cannot start until the first one is completed. Each activity has an

Below:
Complex track layouts such as that formerly at the south end of York station are expensive to maintain and are often poorly laid out for the best approach speeds. This view shows the 14.00 from King's Cross to Inverness arriving at York making a sharp manoeuvre to gain access to Platform 14 on 26 April 1987, before remodelling had been effected there.
Dr W. A. Sharman

expected duration (the most realistic that can be estimated, not the most optimistic). When the network diagram is complete, the sum of the durations through the diagram adds up to the total time the project may take to be completed. The longest path through the diagram is called the 'critical path', because any delay on any activity on the critical path will most likely delay completion of the whole project. Other paths through the diagram have some slack time in them. This slack time (or 'float' in planning-speak) gives the project manager some scope to arrange work in the most effective way. All the time, however, he has to concentrate on keeping the 'critical' activities on time in the most cost-effective way possible.

This puts a different view on planning to that held by many lay people.

Planning does not just involve laying out the best possible way of implementing a series of linked activities. It also involves driving that plan into action, and managing the critical features of it so that completion on time can be confidently expected, barring totally unforeseeable events. The plan is therefore very much a 'live' thing, being constantly changed and updated as events unfold and as achievements are attained.

Sometimes experience proves the original plan to have been too pessimistic. The ECML plan was like this at first, being based on previous experiences with other schemes which had not gone perhaps as smoothly. So it proved possible, around two years into the ECML plan, for it to be confidently announced that Leeds would receive

electric trains a year earlier than had originally been thought possible.

Planning is not however just the managing of activities against time targets. The whole job has to be kept within the costs estimated, or there can be very serious consequences. (In the past a number of schemes have had to be reduced in scope to keep the total cost within the authorised budget.) Cost overruns are in fact very much related to how well the original plan was constructed, and to how closely the work runs to the plan. There is nothing that soaks up money more than a project which is running late. The Humber Bridge project is not the only one which comes to mind as an example of one in which timescales and costs overran.

In reality, a project like the ECML electrification needs to be packaged in manageable blocks, each with someone held responsible for successful execution of his or her block of work. Each block may well have its own sub-network diagram to assist the process, probably on a computer so that the plan can be kept up to date.

For financial control of the ECML project, each of these work blocks, or geographical packages, was run as a mini-project with its own money authority. It therefore followed that if one

Right:

Stephenson's Royal Border Bridge at Berwick posed a real problem for the planning team. Being a prominent listed structure, the viaduct's visual appearance could be marred by heavy overhead structures, yet there was no choice but to provide something to carry the overhead wires there. This problem was typical of the environmental considerations which had to be made along the route. In this picture, Class 46 1Co-Co1 No 46035 crosses the bridge on 30 January 1981. *Brian Morrison*

Above:

Publicity for the plan. *BR*

Below:

On a weekend when concentrated maintenance preparations were being made for the next week's launch of five InterCity 225 train sets into regular service, most Leeds services were being worked by IC125s. This one is arriving at Grantham on 17 February 1990 on the 12.10 from Leeds to King's Cross.
Colin Boocock

work block was heading towards overspending it could not automatically be subsidised by underspending on another part of the project elsewhere. Every change to the work or alteration (up or down) in expected costs had to be separately authorised by means of a variation order, and variation orders were not given out lightly. In this regime, engineers had to work with close control of their expenditure.

The ECML scheme has a number of success stories to relate. It was the first to be authorised under the new investment procedures which were introduced by the then Transport Secretary,

Nicholas Ridley. Because of BR's careful and complete preparation of the financial case, the project was authorised in only three months from when it was submitted to the Department of Transport.

The careful, albeit simple, cost controls have enabled the scheme's costs to be kept within budget. Parts of the project have been completed in record short timescales, so the project overall is well on target at the time of writing for on-time completion in May 1991. Nowadays, BR's planning and development procedures are more sophisticated. Several more recent projects

Above:
Major track remodelling work requires very detailed planning to ensure there is no, or minimal, disruption to railway traffic. Night and weekend possessions are often the key. At the south approach to York station, track laying is well under way as an IC125 passes close by.
British Rail

Left:
Many bridges were rebuilt or replaced to provide the vertical clearance for the 25kV overhead wires. Here, a new set of reinforced concrete arch spans is swung into place on the existing abutments of an overbridge. Such work has to be planned for times when a complete line blockage would not seriously disrupt train services. *British Rail*

have received authorisation in weeks rather than months when placed before the secretary of state for transport. In this scene, BR is well set to take full advantage of the railway investment boom which is now well under way, and which will transform British Rail's performance in the future. Electrification of the East Coast main line can be said to be the project which started BR's change in fortunes.

4.
Wires Up

The outward and visible sign of a railway which is being electrified is the erection of the structures which will support the overhead wires, and the eventual manifestation of the wires themselves. Other chapters of this book have already shown that there is much more to it than this!

The BR Board has a centralised design group for handling new electrification schemes. For the ECML project this was headed by the overhead system Design Engineer, Philip Clarke, working under the direction of Norman Howard, the Board's Electrification Engineer. This centralisation has enabled the preparation of quite detailed layouts to be achieved in time for the estimates for scheme authorisation to be accurate. Thus it is now possible for the contractors who will supply and erect the equipment to receive detailed drawings soon after a scheme is authorised. This is one feature which has enabled the ECML scheme to get away to such a rapid start when compared with earlier schemes. In earlier years, design was carried out by the contractors, who could not get on with the work in earnest until the scheme was authorised.

The planning of the erection of the overhead equipment on the ECML made much use of track possessions required for other works. There were, for example, possessions needed to enable resignalling work to proceed, and for the track remodellings and realignments outlined in other chapters, as well as for track maintenance in the ordinary course of events. This linking together of different work into joint possessions resulted in the almost complete elimination of delays to trains caused by work on overhead electrification. In this respect the ECML scheme

Above right:
The tall structures needed in order to support the span wires across a four-track section are secured on concrete bases. This view shows some of the first masts for the ECML scheme being put in place. *British Rail*

Right:
The process of digging the hole for a mast and then filling it with concrete is time consuming. *British Rail*

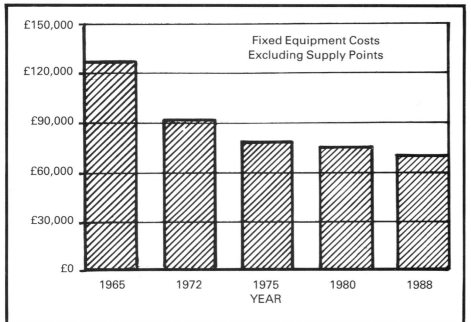

was a substantial improvement on past experience.

Another feature which speeded up the work was the use of piled foundations for overhead support structures. Normal railway practice for decades has been to dig holes at the structure base positions and fill these holes with concrete. Suitable support bolts were let into the top of the concrete blocks on which the masts would be secured, or the mast was 'planted' in a hole left for it in the base and was then grouted in.

This procedure was expensive in many ways. It required a number of consecutive operations, leading to several possessions in order to prepare the foundations for one length of track. Thus the risk of delaying regular traffic was high. The concrete required time to cure, so repeat visits were necessary to complete the process.

Recent BR practice has been to use piled foundations wherever practicable. In this process, a steel tubular column is vibrated vertically into the ground, and the structure mast bolted directly on top of it. It is useful for two-track sections of railway where the horizontal loading on the masts due to wire tensions is containable. The method is very fast in operation, enabling four to five masts to be erected in an hour. (The record appears to be an occasion when eight piled foundations were vibrated in and their masts erected within 25min!)

There are however many occasions where piled foundations are not suitable. In these cases conventional concrete bases are essential. For example, the masts for headspans over four-track sections could not economically be supported on piles because of their loadings. For the same reason, neither could anchor masts. There are also many ground conditions which are unsuitable for piling, particularly where there are boulders or rock.

The design of wiring system for the East Coast main line scheme was based on the BR Mk 3A system used successfully in earlier schemes, modified to suit the higher train running speeds envisaged, and designated Mk 3B. The need in particular for a top speed of 140mph necessitated increasing the tension in the contact wire in the Mk 3B system to 11kN from the 8.9kN of the former

Mk 3A equipment. The higher tension improves high speed current collection as well as reducing the risk of high winds displacing the wire to the point of pantograph 'blow off'.

The overhead system uses three longitudinal wires, the upper, catenary wire, being used to carry the contact wire using droppers of variable lengths, so arranged as to keep the contact wire at the design height above rail level.

Above and right:
This is the new electric control office at Doncaster, from which the central part of the English end of the East Coast route overhead wire system energisation is maintained and controlled. This control centre uses video screens to display the state of all feeder points and switching stations. *(Both) British Rail*

The third wire is the current return wire which is suspended along the masts at the trackside. On two-track sections, each catenary and contact wire is normally supported from single masts, using cantilever arms and inclined drop brackets. The layout is otherwise conventional. Each contact wire is roughly 1km long, anchored at one end on a trackside mast (known as a mid-point anchor), and tensioned at the other end by a system of weights and pulleys suspended from another mast. These end masts in particular carry strong bending forces and need heavy concrete bases and stay wires. All mast structures are directly bonded to the running rails by cables, to ensure effective earthing.

Wider track layouts, including three- and four-track sections, no longer require the heavy bridge structures which epitomised electrification around Crewe for example. The catenary wires are supported from double span wires, which bridge the tracks from mast to mast. This is a much cheaper and relatively environment-friendly method. Its only serious disadvantage when compared with bridge spans is what can happen when an accident or a broken insulator brings down the wires. If a span wire is affected it is likely that traffic has to be stopped on all routes under the span due to displacement of the contact wires.

All catenary and contact wires are insulated from earthed structures by means of insulators. New materials for the manufacture of insulators are used in vandal-prone areas where impact resistance is necessary to protect them from evilly-inspired projectiles. Clearances between catenary wires and the undersides of bridges and tunnels have been further reduced by 50mm to 150mm. This is a big enough gap for electrical safety (except when an unsuspecting pigeon bridges the gap, when the pigeon, fatally unaware of what it has done, can bring out the protective circuit breakers in the nearest switching station). Test runs to ensure that pantographs on locomotives can run at high speeds without coming off the wires were carried out using the DM&EE's *Mentor* laboratory coach. The author has seen this high speed test vehicle, which carries a pantograph which can be observed from a raised roof window, marshalled in a service HST between the guard's vehicle (the TGS) and the adjacent powercar.

WE'RE GOING LIVE!

DANGER

East Coast Main Line ELECTRIFICATION

An exciting result of the new design and erection methods for the overhead line has been the reduction in installation costs when compared with previous schemes on BR. The graph shows what has been achieved since 25kV electrification of main lines was first attempted in Britain. The costs on which the graph is based are all adjusted to 1989 price levels to show the improvement in real terms.

Electricity from the national grid is taken at 16 locations, normally at 132kV though at two points the 275kV network is tapped. The substations transform the supply down to the nominal 25kV single phase supply for distribution to the BR system.

The overhead network is controlled from three electric control offices, at Hornsey, Doncaster and Cathcart, Glasgow, the latter shared with the Scottish electrified routes and the northern end of the WCML. The new control room at Doncaster uses the latest microprocessor technology with video displays completely replacing the traditional large system diagram. This is the first time on BR that a video

system has not been backed up by a mimic diagram. The video enables sections of the overhead line to be isolated for maintenance or repair work, and indicates immediately when there has been a circuit breaker trip which might result from a fault or an incident on the railway. There are some 46 lineside switching stations at which the system can be isolated in an emergency or for planned maintenance work.

Not all overhead line structures have been to the standard designs. There was much upset over the thought of electric overhead catenary crossing the Royal Border Bridge at Berwick, in view of the historic nature of that structure. The situation was rescued by the use of slimmer structures designed by consulting engineer Ove Arup.

Construction of the overhead network was centred on four new depots at Peterborough, Doncaster, Newcastle and Millerhill (Edinburgh). Following completion of construction work, the ongoing maintenance of the system will be based on depots at Peterborough, Doncaster, Morpeth and Millerhill. Short-possession work on the wiring such as replacing damaged droppers or registration arms or insulators will be handled using small, rail-mounted work trolleys, a much more sensible solution than dragging out a complete wiring train each time anything needs attention. There are however two wiring trains to cover the Eastern Region section of the ECML which are needed when it is necessary to renew or replace worn or damaged lengths of contact wire or catenary, and ScotRail has its train as well.

That this chapter has been longer than the author originally expected testifies to the hidden complexity of overhead wiring and distribution. There is however very much more to it than can be explained here.

One vital point that cannot be overstressed is how dangerous the system is if approached too closely: 25,000V can kill instantly. A victim who is not killed can still find himself stunned, or burned beyond recall. That is why the training of British Rail personnel who work on or near electrified tracks is so carefully directed towards adopting safe methods of working. That is why it is vital that everyone treats an electrified railway with the respect it deserves, and avoids *any* unauthorised access or trespass.

This message has to be broadcast far and wide each time electrification extends into a new area. Local people do not always understand how lethal the wires are. Nor do they appreciate that the wires are always live, even when there appears to be no traffic on the railway. To get the message across, the Regions have used a number of campaigns. Schools are visited by the British Transport Police, because the adventurousness of young people makes them more vulnerable to danger. Over a million schoolchildren have been confronted with the stark message that safety is paramount, and an electric railway can kill.

Even within the railway, staff need reminding when a section goes 'live', and a special campaign is directed at them, supported by posters which name the energisation date.

5.
The New Trains

What is it that makes the new InterCity 225 trains so special? Their sleek, rakish looks? Their record-breaking potential? Their innovative technical design? What is it that makes them so much better than the already excellent IC125 High Speed Trains which they replace?

Previous chapters have already explained that Britain's rail speed record for locomotives was gained by a Class 91 when its test train reached 162mph. This speed is so close to the near-163mph recorded by an Advanced Passenger Train as to make little difference, and the APT was not classed as a locomotive-hauled train in any case!

The specification for the InterCity 225 trains was extremely demanding. They had to have a designed operating speed of 140mph (225kph) to meet future business aspirations. The locomotives were required to be compatible with standard BR rolling stock (unlike the IC125s which have different buffing and train supply arrangements) so that the '91s' could haul sleeping car and other trains between their periods of IC225 running. The coaches were to ride as well at 140mph as the BR Mk 3 coaches did at 125mph — quite a challenge. The new trains were required to provide an economic solution to the problem of improving on the operating costs of the IC125 sets at the same time as marking a significant improvement in customer comfort and amenity. The InterCity 225 was intended to become InterCity's new flagship. All these aims have, I submit, been successfully achieved.

The locomotives represent a novel, but generally conventional solution. They are novel in the mechanical layout of their traction motors, and in the asymmetrical design of the locomotive bodies. All other features are generally conventional, in the sense that they are of proven, but very much up to date, technical design, some of which builds on the experience gained with BR's former Advanced Passenger Train powercars.

The contract for supply of the 31 Class 91 locomotives was let to GEC Transportation Projects early in 1986. GEC subcontracted the then BR-owned company BREL to assemble the locomotives in its works at Crewe. This

Above:
At King's Cross, No 91007 (left) heads a nine-coach rake of Mk 4 stock for a Pullman working while No 91006 is at the front of a standard eight-car InterCity 225 rake forming the 15.10 to Leeds on 7 March 1990.
Colin Boocock

arrangement enabled British Rail to have a proper commercial relationship with the main supplier, with special provisions for the contractor to warrant the performance of the locomotives.

The design, manufacture and assembly of the first Class 91 locomotive took just two years, an exceptionally short time. That gave GEC and BR engineers sufficient time for performance testing and mileage accumulation running before putting the locomotives into service.

The design of the '91' demonstrates considerable mechanical ingenuity. A high speed locomotive has to deliver considerable power, in this case almost 7,000hp at its 1hr rating, or 6,000hp continuously. The locomotive has also to be of relatively light weight if it is not to cause damage to track at the higher speeds. The specification of the Class 91 also required the locomotives to be capable of hauling tilting coaches, should they have to do so on future West Coast main line duties. That meant that they had to be able to curve at up to 9° cant deficiency, putting even greater demands on their ability to be kind to the tracks they would run on. Yet they also had to be capable of hauling heavy trains of sleeping cars on either

the West or East Coast routes, including the climbs over Shap and Beattock. Thus the Class 91 had to be sure-footed, powerful, lightweight and kind to the track. Such a challenge might have been met by some manufacturers with expensive use of new technology, taking BR close to the frontiers of invention. GEC's design experts, led by Engineer Mike Newman, were able to put together a design package which demonstrated clear, objective thinking, resulting in a very neat locomotive design indeed, which met its specification well.

The locomotive is configured as a Bo-Bo of 84 tons weight. In appearance the leading end is streamlined, the other end blunt, so as to minimise air drag between the locomotive and the train it is hauling. However, there is a full-width driving cab at the blunt end, to enable the locomotive to haul trains conventionally, either way round, when not working IC225 sets. The blunt end cab is neatly styled, to provide a pleasant aspect when leading but not to be too prominent when marshalled next to the train.

To enable track forces to be minimised and to reduce body sway, innovation has been employed in the following areas of design:

● The transformer is slung below the underframe (EMU fashion), which lowers the centre of gravity of the body significantly.
● The traction motors are suspended from the body underframe, occupying the space which they would have done had they been bogie mounted.
● Other heavy equipment such as the main compressor is also under the body.
● The bogie design is not unlike that of the APT powercars, having excellent curving and wheelset steering capabilities.
● Unsprung axle weight is also reduced by having the main brake discs located on the traction motor shafts, off the bogie completely.

The configuration of the traction motor drive design is critical to the track force equation. The key to low track forces is to minimise the unsprung weight on each axle. In conventional designs the traction motors are mounted in the bogie frames, and on high speed locomotives they have the drive arranged through some form of linked or quill drive so as not to hang the motors directly on the axles, though axle-hung motors can be quite satisfac-

Above left:
Driving van trailer No 82206 is the leading vehicle of the 11.10 to London King's Cross as the train is propelled out of Leeds station on 7 March 1990 by locomotive No 91007.
Colin Boocock

Left:
The 11.10 from King's Cross to Leeds with No 91007 at the head of a rake of new Mk 4 coaches has the air of a fine high speed formation as it passes Werrington, north of Peterborough, on 16 February 1990.
Dr W. A. Sharman

Above:
The wide entrance vestibules and inter-vehicle gangway connections are a highly significant design feature of the Mk 4 coaches. The welcoming atmosphere is enhanced by the bright red matting in the standard class carriage vestibules. *British Rail*

Above right:
In the InterCity 225 trains there is copious provision of British Telecom card-phones. The large sliding door on the left of this vestibule is for the larger toilet, suitable for invalids, which doubles as a changing room. *British Rail*

Right:
Class 91 locomotive bogie showing traction motors and drives. *Courtesy GEC-Alsthom*

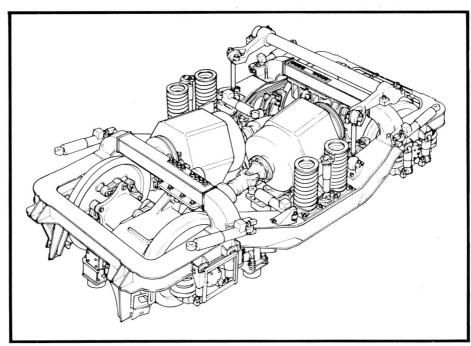

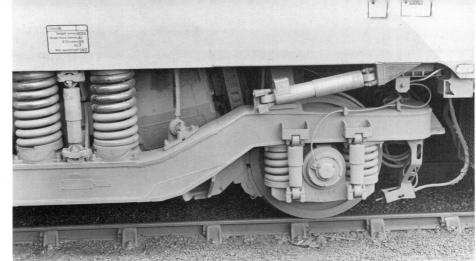

tory on locomotives for lower speeds. Even with quill drives, most of the weight is on the bogie frames, which increases the dynamic forces which the bogies transmit to the rails.

On the Class 91 each motor is suspended flexibly from the locomotive body, at an angle such that it is possible to fit in a short, stubby, cardan shaft with universal joints and variable length, able to take up the movement between the body and the wheels. At the lower end of the shaft is a gearbox, capable of transmitting the high power of the motor to a hollow quill drive shaft linked at one end to the wheelset. The gearboxes and other drive components have been extensively tested by GEC on laboratory rigs at its factories, to ensure performance meets the specification.

Flexible suspension apart, the traction motors are otherwise conventional dc machines, but with their shafts extended upwards so that the brake discs can be mounted at the free end of each motor's armature shaft. The locomotive's braking from high speed uses rheostatic deceleration down to 35mph to 20mph during which range mechanical braking is blended in as the rheostatic braking fades away. The motor-mounted disc brakes are supplemented by single brake block actuators, one against each wheel tread.

The locomotive power circuits use well proven thyristor phase angle control to supply the traction motors with smoothed dc current over the voltage range needed. The motors have separately excited fields, supported by a micro-processor controlled wheelslip control system which maximises adhesion. This is fed information about speed by a radar device, which enables locomotive speed and wheel rotation speeds to be compared by the equipment which can control each motor separately. When high tractive effort is required in poor rail adhesion conditions, the motors can be controlled accurately by the wheelslip equipment to enable the wheels to operate with that minimal slip which ensures maximum transmitted tractive effort. Thus, although the Class 91 is only an 84-ton Bo-Bo, it is well able to use its 7,000hp potential for heavy train haulage.

The locomotive carries receiver equipment enabling it to be controlled from a driving van trailer coach cab at the other end of the train. This system uses time division multiplex (TDM) equipment to feed low voltage control pulses along the train wires, so that the driver's control instructions can be translated in the locomotive.

The coaches through which the control pulses are transmitted have been supplied by Metro-Cammell of Birmingham, now also part of GEC/Alstholm. Each train set was originally intended to consist of eight intermediate vehicles. Traffic growth has resulted in an order for 31 additional vehicles to be supplied at the end of the delivery,

12412

so that each set can be strengthened to nine passenger-carrying coaches.

The Mk 4 coach bodyshell is a monocoque stressed skin welded steel structure. Bodyshells have been supplied by BREL Derby and at least 80 by Breda of Italy. Quite late in the order, BREL transferred production of Mk 4 bodies to its works at Crewe. The bodies are assembled complete with windows and doors, and are externally painted prior to being delivered to Metro-Cammell's works at Washwood Heath. Metro-Cammell fits out the carriage interiors, drops the bodies on to the SIG bogies, gives the vehicles their final tests and makes them up into full rakes of eight coaches plus the driving van trailer (of which more later).

Inside the Mk 4 coaches the customer will find new features. The seat layouts break up the conventional arrangement whereby seats are sited in bays opposite one another. The standard class saloons have a mixture of face-to-face and face-to-back seats, arranged so that everyone gets a view through the regularly spaced windows.

In the first class, the grey decor is actually remarkably restful. Here, the two-plus-one seat layout is reversed, side to side at the mid-point of the vehicle. This enables the appearance of the interior to be broken up so that the

'long tube' effect is minimised. As in the standard class, there are irregularly spaced smoked glass screens which assist in creating this effect.

The toilets are among the best I have seen in railway carriages. Each coach has one large and one small toilet compartment. The large one is designed to serve people in invalid chairs and doubles as a baby-changing room. The baby shelf is hinged and can be dropped down to locate across the

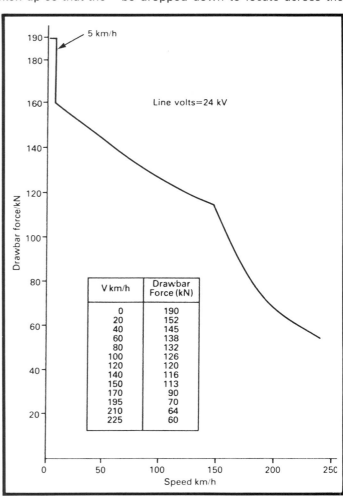

V km/h	Drawbar Force (kN)
0	190
20	152
40	145
60	138
80	132
100	126
120	120
140	116
150	113
170	90
195	70
210	64
225	60

Line volts=24 kV

sink. At last we have hot air hand dryers to add to our comfort!

Catering is based on the trolley module system now well established by InterCity On Board Catering Services. The wider-than-standard gangways between coaches assist the passage of trolleys to each class of accommodation. In the first class coaches, trolleys can be parked in the centre of the vehicle where the seat rows are joggled, which enables customers to get past without discomfort while the attendant is serving others. The kitchen, restaurant and buffet cars are neat, modern and conventional in layout.

Carriage air-conditioning noise is less obtrusive than on Mk 3 stock. Also the two panes in each double glazed side window unit are located further apart in the Mk 4, which is intended to reduce noise transmission from outside. The more rigid bodyside construction when compared with a Mk 3 has another advantage for the customer who likes to work on the table by his seat. When passing a train at high speed on the adjacent track, the table no longer jumps sideways as the bodyside deflects when the passing bow wave hits it!

Exterior doors are of the swing plug type, operated by passengers by depressing buttons. The buttons are illuminated when the guard has released them; when they are not illuminated the doors are safely locked.

The Mk 4 coach stands on two SIG bogies of a design which is claimed to work well at up to 160mph. The bogie frame is a short design without headstocks. The frame sides are deeply depressed so that the air secondary springs carry the coach at a height which does not transmit bogie pitch frequencies. Primary suspension consists of coil springs directly over the axleboxes, controlled by outboard hydraulic dampers. There is also roll control, lateral damping between the body and bogies, vertical damping by the secondary air springs, and large, prominent yaw dampers to prevent bogie instability at high speed.

The bogies give a firm, controlled ride which actually improves as speed rises. Performance at 125mph and above is impressive, particularly when one recognises the inherent simplicity of the bogie design.

The Mk 4 coach sets are coupled within the sets by fixed head tightlock couplers. This enables braking and traction shocks to be avoided. It also supports the policy of keeping each train set together permanently, so that each maintenance and overhaul is carried out on the whole set at one operation.

At the far end of the train from the locomotive is the matching driving van trailer, a recently evolved concept. Policy is clear that, on high speed trains worked by push-pull methods, the leading vehicle must be substantial, capable of withstanding high speed collision with animals and objects on the track, and must not therefore carry passengers. The answer to this conundrum is a van with driving cab, and which can carry parcels, mails and luggage, together with the guard. InterCity first introduced this concept on the West Coast main line in 1988. The driving van trailers (DVTs) on the East Coast route are similar, but styled to conform with the Mk 4 coach profile. They have streamlined cab fronts which are similar to the Class 91 locomotives.

The first '91'-hauled train arrived at Leeds in March 1989. Introduction of Mk 4 coaches to the King's Cross-Leeds service began in October 1989. By July 1991 we shall see the full operation of InterCity 225 services to Newcastle and Edinburgh. The transformation will be complete.

Or will it? In fact, the East Coast route will still be host to IC125 units after the electrification scheme is complete. For a start, those trains which run through from King's Cross to Hull and Cleethorpes are expected to continue as IC125s because of the need to provide good quality through trains. At the time of writing it is planned that those trains which extend beyond Edinburgh to Aberdeen and Inverness will be formed of IC125s throughout. This acknowledges that there has been some growth since the scheme was originally conceived, and neatly solves the problem of how to avoid customers having to change trains at Waverley.

The replacement for the present-day IC125 train between King's Cross, Edinburgh and Glasgow Queen Street will make use of the additional electrification achieved between Carstairs and Edinburgh, so that Class 91-hauled trains from King's Cross will be able to run direct from Edinburgh to Glasgow Central via Carstairs and Motherwell.

In appearance, a complete InterCity 225 train set comprising Class 91 locomotive, eight or nine Mk 4 carriages, and a DVT, presents a sleek, exciting, and modern image — a true and valued successor to the InterCity 125 High Speed Train, and one of which the present director of InterCity, Dr John Prideaux, can justly be proud.

6.
The First Electrics

Although the InterCity 225 trains were to be the stars of the electrified East Coast main line, they were not the first electric trains to take advantage of the energised overhead wires which previously had extended from King's Cross only to Hitchin before branching off on the Royston line. Indeed the first electric additions to the regular passenger services on the main line were not even trains belonging to the sponsoring InterCity business!

Planned to begin operating out of Peterborough from October 1987, electric multiple-unit services of Network SouthEast actually began running a limited public service between King's Cross and Huntingdon late in 1986. The first full extended service of electric trains was the hourly commuter run from Peterborough to King's Cross which began on 11 May 1987. This was inaugurated at the time when NSE was still operating Class 312 EMUs on the Great Northern outer suburban services. Local dignitaries in Peterborough and Huntingdon had already been given a sight of a modern Class 317

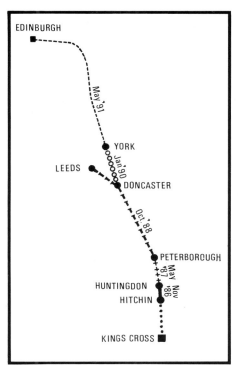

EMU however, to whet their appetites for the trains which would quickly (in 1988) become the standard for the route. Growth on these services has been phenomenal, rising to over 30% and requiring the provision of an additional 11 EMUs!

As soon as the wires were energised, training of train crew and others in electric locomotives was begun by introducing them to the Brush/Hawker Siddeley Class 89 Co-Co No 89001. This 125mph, 104-ton, 5,380hp locomotive had been delivered in 1986 as a prototype to prove the technology for running a Co-Co locomotive at high

Left:
Introduction of ECML electric services.

Below:
The Class 312s were the first electric trains to work in regular interval service to Peterborough. During 1989 Class 317s from the West Coast main line displaced the '312s', thus raising the quality of these Network SouthEast outer suburban services. A '317' on the 14.30 from Peterborough to King's Cross passes Holme on 16 February 1990. *Dr W. A. Sharman*

speeds. For a time it was thought that it might be required as the East Coast route standard machine, but the decision to go for a higher speed, higher power Bo-Bo (the Class 91) effectively removed its original purpose. There was speculation that the '89's' Co-Co arrangement and heavier weight would suit it to the West Coast route inclines over Shap and Beattock, and it did indeed perform effectively in tests on that route.

However, having been funded by InterCity, No 89001 was put to early use on the East Coast route, firstly on crew training and later on a regular commuter diagram which included the 17.36 from King's Cross to Peterborough. It was indeed the first electric locomotive to take a train into Leeds, which it achieved shortly after energisation had been proved, in August 1988. Having been fitted out for push-pull operation using TDM equipment in 1989, No 89001 picked up a regular diagram in 1990 working one of the two sets of InterCity Mk 2f coaches which had been fitted out with additional seating for longer distance commuter work.

The Class 91s began to be delivered early in 1988. Following very extensive proving trials a small number of the first 10 locomotives was put into revenue-earning service in order to accumulate service running experience. This type of running is an absolute essential in the development of a modern locomotive. Intensive mileage accumulation when only a few examples have been delivered enables any unforeseen technical problems to be identified at an early stage. In the case of the Class 91s there were clearly some development modifications to make, as in effect the early locomotives were being used in place of the prototype for which there had been no time to build. The results of the modifications were excellent, and it proved possible to diagram several Class 91 locomotives on King's Cross-Leeds trains from the spring of 1989, much sooner than originally planned.

Preparations for this could have been hampered by the lack of Mk 4 train sets, which (quite correctly, as planned) had not been delivered by then. This is where the engineers' ingenuity came to the rescue of their own need for Class 91 mileage accumulation, as the InterCity business's need to see some public benefit from its new locomotives.

The only trains available for the Class 91s to pull were the erstwhile IC125s. However, the InterCity 125 Mk 3 coaches are not compatible with other BR InterCity trains because of their three-phase ac electric train supply. Other BR locomotive-hauled trains use a single phase supply, capable of taking either ac or dc current, and the Class 91 was equipped to deliver a

Right:

Before the Mk 4 coaches and their driving van trailers became available, a service was operated with Class 91 locomotives using InterCity 125 Mk 3 stock with one IC125 power car converted as a driving trailer. No 43013 is under diesel power at the head of the 16.14 to King's Cross on 6 May 1989 as the train leaves Leeds with a Class 91 providing the main power source at the rear. This view shows the conventional buffer beam and coupling provided on the 'surrogate DVT'.
Colin Boocock

Below:
Class 91 Bo-Bo No 91003 takes the 11.10 from King's Cross towards Leeds near Beeston on 14 October 1989. The Mk 3 InterCity 125 formation has a 'surrogate DVT' at the rear.
Dr L. A. Nixon

single phase supply to its Mk 4 coaches. To overcome this clash, a quite unique scheme was evolved.

The plan was to use the Class 91 locomotives on trains made up of Mk 3 carriages from IC125 sets, using one IC125 powercar as a driving trailer, so that the Class 91 could be driven from it push-pull fashion. The power unit on the driving trailer would be operational, set to provide at idling speed the three-phase train electric supply. The IC125 powercar would be fitted with buffers and drawgear so that the train sets could be hauled by ordinary locomotives if need be, or if the TDM push-pull gear was non-operational.

The converted IC125 powercars could work as normal powercars when attached to InterCity 125 sets, or as 'surrogate driving van trailers' when electrically hauled. The formation of a Class 91-hauled interim InterCity train would therefore be:

● Class 91+8 HST trailer Mk 3s+ 'surrogate DVT'.

In traffic the surrogate DVTs' power units proved not to be satisfactory when continually being run at idling speed. The decision was taken therefore to allow them to run under power as if they were still part of a full IC125 set. The addition of an extra 2,250hp to the 6,000hp-plus of the Class 91 gave performance on the ECML a new, if temporary uplift!

From May 1989 a number of diagrams was turned over to Class 91 operation with Mk 3 stock and surrogate DVTs, all between London and Leeds, working to existing IC125 timings. Reliability of the Class 91s steadily improved. At the time of writing it has reached a very satisfactory level indeed, entirely vindicating the decision to miss out the locomotive prototype stage.

The Mk 4 carriages first appeared on the main line in summer 1989, and entered operation on the 'Yorkshire

Left:
Continuation of overhead line construction with the resultant isolation of some existing electric sections led to some weekend diesel haulage of InterCity 225 formations. On 21 May 1989 Class 47 diesel electric No 47816 leaves King's Cross hauling No 91006 and the 09.15 Sunday Leeds service. *Nick Bartlett*

Below left:
Once the Brush Co-Co No 89001 *Avocet* had been fitted with time-division-multiplex push-pull equipment, it was not long before the Class 89 was seen on Mk 4 formations on the Leeds expresses. On 16 February 1990 it was photographed north of Peterborough with the 12.10 from King's Cross. *Dr W. A. Sharman*

Below:
The sight of a '91' running blunt end first on a conventional train has been described as 'a bit like a 2-6-4T running backwards'! No 91006 passes Doncaster on 6 May 1989 with the InterCity charter train from Carlisle, the 'Thames Eden Express', which it has taken over at Leeds. *Colin Boocock*

Pullman' roster in October of that year. A second train set of Mk 4s was put into service towards the end of the year, and in February 1990 a total of five train sets was in regular daily operation between King's Cross and Leeds. By May 1990 this total had risen to eight, including regular appearance on the 06.00 from York to London.

Class 91s also appeared on other trains, not part of the push-pull framework. For example, a number of charter trains, particularly off the Settle & Carlisle line, provided an opportunity for electric locomotive haulage between Leeds and London. Occasionally the Class 89 would be used, but the normal power on a southbound charter train was (and is) a Class 91 running blunt end forward, in which formation it is limited to 110mph. Your author found the sight a little odd at first, but soon recognised the aesthetic similarity between it and a steam 2-6-4T running bunker first!

While the Class 91s were under construction at Crewe BREL works, a parallel building line in the same workshop was turning out Class 90 Bo-Bo electric locomotives, initially for West Coast main line services. This was part of a BREL contract which subcontracted the traction equipment to GEC, exactly the reverse of the arrangement for the Class 91s!

The Class 90 was conceived as a straight development of the well estab-

lished Class 87 WCML Bo-Bo, using the same bogies and traction motor designs but with more modern, and well proven, thyristor control equipment. The locomotive was intended for mixed traffic working, and was designed to produce around 5,000hp at its continuous rating, and for a maximum speed of 110mph.

At the time of writing (January 1991) the Class 90 locomotives for main line freight and parcels services are being delivered to Willesden and Crewe depots for commissioning and mileage accumulation. Some of these locomotives have been painted in BR's standard main line livery, and others in Railfreight's multi-tone grey with decals. The latter forms part of a pool of electric locomotives dedicated to the Railfreight Sector services, not specifically allocated to either the East or West Coast routes. The first roster for a Railfreight Class 90 to reach the author's eyes was on a train for demountable freight being inaugurated in 1990 from Harwich to Warrington and Gushetfaulds in Glasgow on a 90mph schedule, using the West Coast route.

Full utilisation of electric locomotives on long distance freight and parcels trains via the ECML will clearly only be possible when the wires are energised right through to the northeast and to Scotland. This will be happening at the time this book appears in print.

7.
Track Changes

There are those who believe that the role played by the civil engineers in a major electrification scheme is basic and dull: just the business of making room under bridges and tunnel roofs for overhead wires, replacing complex track layouts with simple ones and adjusting a few alignments here and there. How wrong they are!

In fact, the civil engineer is quite fundamental to the ability of the other engineering departments to implement their parts of a project such as East Coast main line electrification. It is not all dull, basic engineering by any means. A civil engineer, more than anyone else who physically changes the railway infrastructure, has a potentially major impact on the environment. This chapter explores a number of interesting mini-projects which were enacted to satisfy the fears of people around the country. Many folk were concerned about the potential for a

Right:
Simplifying the track layout at a major station like York, at the same time as smoothing the alignment for approaching trains, involves considerable work on site. Space has to be cleared for the larger radius curves, and much new ballast is spread before the track panels can be placed in position and lined up.
British Rail

Below:
York station layout as it was. *BR*

Below right:
York station layout by June 1989. *BR*

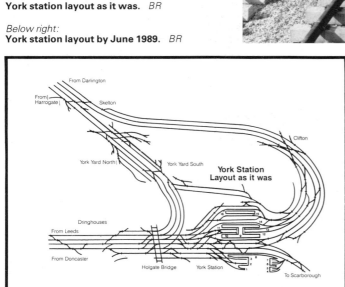

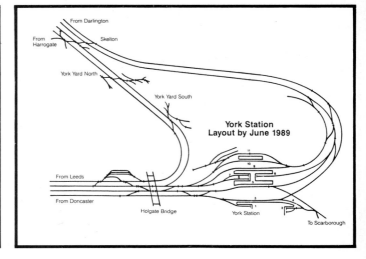

Left:

Track simplification has uncluttered the interior of York station to a considerable extent. This view of the 16.35 IC125 to King's Cross leaving from Platform 3 also shows how unobtrusive is the overhead 25kV wiring. *Colin Boocock*

Below left:

Getting concrete up to unusual heights demands ingenuity from the railways' civil engineers! Here one can see concrete being pumped up from road vehicles to the deck of Durham viaduct. It must be a Sunday! *British Rail*

scheme such as this to spoil what had been well known beauty spots or structures of historical interest.

Bridge clearances did certainly have to be increased. Few were subjected to media-drawing destruction such as exploding away the arches. One of those that were so blown up was used to engender a little local excitement by getting a 10-year-old schoolboy to press the destruction plunger. Indeed, the senior civil engineers such as Eastern Region's Philip Payne (since succeeded by Colin Schofield) and ScotRail's Gavin Burns have been quite forward in putting their activities in the public eye through newspapers and television news reports, encouraged and supported by the public affairs managers of the two Regions.

Some bridge decks were lifted out of the way by large cranes, to be replaced by modern, aesthetically pleasant structures whose slimmer dimensions allowed the wires to pass underneath. Other overbridges were left untouched because, for example, to raise them would upset the gradients on the road over them too much. In these cases, the more expensive choice was adopted of lowering the tracks through the bridges. This is usually quite costly because of the need to keep approach gradients on the railway small and digging is always expensive.

Below left:

Newcastle route rationalisation and resignalling – old layout. *BR*

Below:

Newcastle route rationalisation and resignalling – new layout. *BR*

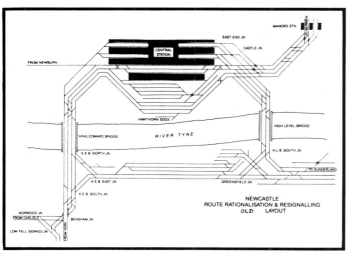

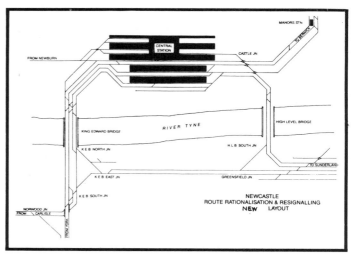

Left:
To preserve the stucture of the ancient viaduct at Durham for future generations of trains it was essential to waterproof the deck. This view shows the impervious layer, with concrete surfacing being applied to it in readiness for ballasting. *British Rail*

Below left:
Raising the station footbridge at Drem on the Scottish section of the route resulted in this highly original new bridge being provided. The design uses modern materials with a traditional appearance. On 16 October 1989 the 13.52 from Dunbar to Haymarket is stopping there. *Tom Noble*

crossings in a complex track layout has many advantages. Fewer routes need fewer signals; fewer point ends need much less maintenance; and any reduction in the number of flat crossings saves considerable expense in track maintenance costs. When new signalling schemes are mooted, it often makes sense to remodel the layout as well, so that the new signalling system is as simple as it sensibly can be.

One little-understood factor which helped BR in much of its work on the ECML was the level of grant support from the European Regional Development Fund, totalling some £47 million. Much of this was directed at the works in the Northeast of England as a means of injecting European Community funds into areas needing technical rejuvenation.

Durham viaduct proved a difficult scheme to implement with the acceptance of local councils and people. It was necessary to provide overhead structures, to the simplified Ove Arup design. At the same time, considerable work needed to be done on the viaduct itself to waterproof it and otherwise fit it for another century or so of operations. Some conservationists wanted BR to leave a gap in the wires right across the viaduct, with third rail collection (or a battery equivalent on the locomotives). Fortunately common sense has resulted in a satisfactorily neat design which is less obtrusive than was feared. It has also been possible to realign the platform at Durham with two spin-off advantages: trains can approach the platform loop at 40mph instead of 20mph, and the overhead wire clearance from the station's awning has been preserved without having to cut the awning back.

It was not that easy at Morpeth, another station on a curve in a conservation area. This time the delightfully decorative awning was moved bodily back from the platform edge by over 3ft, thus preserving intact a listed structure. The movement of this awning structure was carried out during one night (after several weeks of preparation) using lifting jacks to raise the support columns. Slides were inserted beneath them, and hydraulic rams used to push the structure to its new position.

The need for safety also brought about another change to overbridges. Many old bridges have low parapets. These parapets have to be built up so that people on the bridges cannot by any reasonable means either touch the overhead cables or bring something they are holding into contact with them.

New track layouts for railway operating take advantage of the new situation in which virtually all passenger trains are unit trains without the need to run round locomotives at termini or to hold them between trips. Thus, track simplification can be employed without reducing the capacity of the layout to handle the future traffic on offer. A simplified layout often gives a bonus because the extra space generated by simplification leaves room to realign tracks for higher speeds. Even on station approaches this can save useful seconds or even minutes on timings. Indeed, the history of train speeds on the ECML is one of continuous improvement by continually picking away at small but cumulative opportunities to upgrade places where speeds have to be restricted due to alignment problems.

Thus the diagram which shows the new approach layout to York has brought with it the sight of InterCity trains entering York station from the north and south at higher approach speeds than previously thought possible. The impact of not having to release locomotives and stable them at odd locations has been one factor which has enabled York station to lose its two through tracks, a change which has altered the appearance of the interior of that historic station considerably.

Further north, at Newcastle, the famous crossings at the north end of the station below the castle have gone, replaced by a much leaner layout. The act of removing so many points and

Scotland had its fair share of engineering work, too, much of which has occupied the Region's Project Manager, Don Thatcher. A major, if virtually unseen, operation was the singling and relining of the south bore of Calton Tunnel just outside Waverley station. The tunnel was previously a bare rock tunnel and its inside condition did not suit the prospect of either raising its roof or lowering the floor. Track singling was a clear winner, but to guarantee the condition of the tunnel for the next century or so necessitated some dramatic work inside it. Completely circular lining sections were bolted together and fixed to the rock with around 1,000 rock bolts, and then the space between the linings and the original walls was filled with grout. The tunnel is now much strengthened and well suited for its future role.

On a much smaller scale was the replacement of the old footbridge at Drem by a new, fabricated one which combined modern design with the traditional. Many other bridges had to be raised or replaced in Scotland, including the big footbridge across the west end of Waverley station.

In all these activities the local authorities were closely involved, as were conservation agencies and other press-ure groups. As a result, some activities cost more than they otherwise would, but all people concerned are content that the result is acceptable. The East Coast men only have to point to what was done between Crewe and Manchester and Liverpool in the 1950s to see how much progress has been made in the way these environmental matters are tackled today.

8.
Signal Success

The East Coast main line is controlled from surprisingly few signalboxes, or, signalling centres as the largest ones are known. Fig 10 shows that King's Cross signalling centre covers the ECML from the terminus as far as Sandy (exclusive). Peterborough centre then picks up control and covers the main line to between Stoke and Highdyke, where the Doncaster centre takes over the signalling.

Doncaster also controls the Leeds line as far as the approach to South Elmsall where the Leeds signalling area begins. Doncaster centre's northern boundary on the main line is between Shaftholme (where the former Eastern and North Eastern Regions once met) and Templehirst. From there the modern signalling centre at York takes over, right through to Northallerton, where it meets up with the new Tyneside control area.

Eleven miles north of Newcastle begins the stretch controlled by three smaller boxes. The first of these is Morpeth, which itself hands over control after 17 miles to Alnmouth box. Another 19 miles later the main line enters the control area of Tweedmouth box. From the Scottish border to Waverley station all control comes under Edinburgh signalling centre.

Signal control uses track circuit block, with signal spacings designed for high speed trains running at 2min headways between London and Newcastle. (By timetabling headways at 5min minimum, there is allowed some sensible flexibility in running including the effect of speed restrictions.) As built, the systems were not suitable entirely for use alongside a 25kV electrified railway, and considerable immunisation work has been necessary in order to prevent induced ac voltages adversely affecting track circuits and signalling.

This immunisation work has included the substitution of copper cabling by optical (glass fibre) cables. Optical cables are a modern development. Originally selected for long distance transmission of data flows because of the transmission clarity of glass fibre cables, they have the excellent side effect of being non-conductive and thus immune from interference from outside electrical sources. Optical cables are used for telecommunications circuits which carry both voice and vital control circuits. They were given some publicity when a trunk cable was ceremoniously joined together by the then Eastern Region General Manager, David Rayner.

The signalling centres in London, Peterborough, Doncaster, Leeds and Edinburgh were all built between 1967 and 1979, and thus use standard relay type interlocking for route setting and signalling.

The new centres at York and Tyneside use solid state interlocking (SSI), and the three smaller boxes at Morpeth, Alnmouth and Tweedmouth have also been provided with new SSI equipment and new panels.

Solid state interlocking uses microprocessors to carry out the functions formerly done by relay systems. By using computer logic, the size of the installation is very, very much reduced. The reliability of the equipment is excellent, and needs much less physical maintenance than do mechanical relays.

Reliability of solid state interlocking, and thus operational safety of the railway, is assured by the use of three processors for each set of key interlocking functions. Each of the three pro-

Left:
ECML signalling control areas.

Below:
Signalling schemes prior to the electrification of the East Coast main line, as well as those associated with it, have swept away the once familiar semaphore signals which littered the approaches to stations and yards. North of York, this 125 set was working the 11.30 from King's Cross to Dundee on 27 May 1985.
Dr W. A. Sharman

EDINBURGH

TWEEDMOUTH
ALNMOUTH
MORPETH
TYNE

YORK

LEEDS

DONCASTER

Signalling Centre ■

Signal Box ○

Approximate Boundary
Between Control —┼—
Areas

PETERBOROUGH

KINGS CROSS

and correct the fault. The system will only fail if two processors fail together. According to ER Signal Engineer (Projects) Roger Pope, this has been predicted as being likely only once in every 196 years for each group of three processors, and failure is in any case a fail-safe action. A single processor cannot be allowed to operate the system on its own.

The SSI equipment for interlocking at all locations covered by the signalling centre is housed at that centre. It sends out operating instructions to trackside modules which translate the electronic information into electric feeds to the points and signals. The data links to the lineside modules are duplicated by diverse routes. Maintenance of the electronic equipment is largely centralised, and response to problems, however rare they may be, is fast.

The three signalboxes between Newcastle and the border which have been fitted out with new SSI equipment each also have to oversee eight or nine level crossings on the high speed route. These are equipped with closed circuit television (CCTV) monitors which enable the signalman to see if any pedestrians or road traffic are within the crossings. The equipment can operate the barriers automatically, but it is essential that the signalman observes that the crossing is clear when the barriers are fully down before he presses the 'crossing clear' button which then allows the railway signals to clear for trains to proceed.

The two new centres at York and Tyneside employ the latest technology in signalling control. They are termed 'integrated electronic control centres' (IECCs). Instead of the conventional control panel on which is mounted the signalling and route-setting buttons, the IECCs use high resolution video screens and terminals to display the track and train situation in the area and to initiate commands. With electronic processors handling the control information it becomes possible to add a number of new facilities for the signalmen.

One key feature is automatic route setting. The equipment has in its memory the working timetable for its area, complete with the train description codes for each train, including a daily update of specials. Using programmed logic, the computer selects the most suitable routeing for each train that is handed over to it by each

cessors is identical, and each has exactly the same programs, and each works in exactly the same way. The secret is in the fact that all three have to compare their outputs with each other. Provided all three processors, when given a command to perform an interlocking movement, all come up with the same instruction for the local equipment to perform, when they compare their outputs and find they are the same, the operation can proceed. If one processor fails (at a failure rate of one failure in more than 10,000hr this is rare) the other two processors shut the faulty one down, and carry on working the system, comparing each other's results and initiating operations subject to their outputs being the same. This gives time for the technician to come

neighbouring signalling centre, taking note of the presence of other trains in the area and the timetable priorities of each.

Data from each IECC to the trackside locations is transmitted through telecommunication links using compressed data techniques which enable the instructions being sent 'down the wire' to share cable capacity with countless other electronic messages.

Modern telecommunications systems on the ECML make much use of optical cables. All links used for transmission of signalling and safety instructions are duplicated so that in the event of a cable or equipment failure (even if someone digs a JCB into it!) the operation of the railway can carry on as if all was well, giving the technician time to trace and correct any fault. The alternate duplicate route from York to Tweedmouth is by a series of microwave radio links.

The signalling on the East Coast main line is the familiar BR four-aspect system, three-aspect north of Newcastle. On stretches of plain line, wherever sensible the signalling is automatic, using the occupation of a track circuit by a train to operate the signalling sequence behind it.

An innovation for the ECML is the provision of simplified bidirectional signalling between Northallerton and the Scottish border. This will allow minimum delay to train running during planned engineering work and will cater for flexibility in an emergency during normal operations. It will be possible to permit trains to be looped round a failed train with minimal delay. BR hopes that this facility can be extended to other two-track sections later, particularly to those between Stoke and Doncaster, and to the ECML in Scotland.

Airliners have the facility to record pilot conversations and control actions using the 'black box'. Equally, on SSI installations and in the IECCs, all data is recorded. This provides a vital source of information for enquiries into incidents or accidents on the railway. It is the ability to build on information such as this, plus the greater reliability of modern technology as described in this chapter, which will support the railway in its quest for improving in the future on its already superb safety record.

9.
The New Services

By the time this book appears in print the wires from York to Edinburgh will have been energised, and the railway will be gearing itself up for initiation of full electric working on the ECML to Scotland (it may already have begun!).

Train services are already intense over these lines. From May 1990 the InterCity 125 service from Edinburgh to King's Cross has had its basic hourly frequency increased to half-hourly from 09.30 to 12.30. Newcastle to London is half-hourly virtually all the working day.

The effect of electric traction on these services will be two-fold. Journey speeds from London to Newcastle and Edinburgh will be increased. By how much they will have improved is not published at the time I write this. A 4hr timing to Edinburgh is expected. This will enable the East Coast main line to keep its lead over the West Coast route for many years to come.

The second effect will be passenger carryings, which are expected to rise due to the improved journey times and train quality. To meet that rise in carryings the electric trains will each contain nine Mk 4 coaches, thus enabling individual train lengths to be usefully increased beyond the eight coaches which has been the regular maximum for the IC125s. The potential is there to increase InterCity 225 train lengths further when traffic is high enough to justify 10-coach trains. This would require platform extensions at several locations including King's Cross.

InterCity is also in the commuter business, and is applying resources to it at the southern end of the ECML. Although Peterborough and Huntingdon are in Network SouthEast territory, the peak limited-stop services are the preserve of InterCity. Two trainsets of Mk 2f coaches have been refurbished with additional seating to provide useful carrying capacity on what is becoming a very popular service.

The King's Cross to Leeds line is by now well established as a fast, reliable electrically worked route. Services which penetrate beyond Leeds, to Harrogate or Bradford and which are operating in virtually marginal time

Below:
The standard formation for most 'core' ECML InterCity services is the Class 91 with eight Mk 4 coaches and a DVT. This formation meets the basic needs on London to Leeds, Bradford, Newcastle and Edinburgh and Glasgow services other than Pullman trains and services which are routed off the electrified network. On 16 February 1990 No 91007 heads the 11.10 King's Cross to Leeds north of Peterborough.
Dr W. A. Sharman

keep their Class 91 locomotive attached to the train. A Class 47 locomotive is attached to the leading end for the trip away from the wired routes, the Class 91 locomotive being hauled 'dead' in the train consist. The agreement that both BR InterCity and the West Yorkshire Passenger Transport Authority support electrification between Leeds and Bradford will enable diesel haulage to Bradford to be eliminated.

Services in Scotland which extend 'beyond the wire' are being timetabled to a pattern which is quite different from that envisaged when the project was first being developed. At that time it was intended that each through service from King's Cross to Aberdeen would be formed by removing the Class 91 Bo-Bo at Edinburgh and replacing it with one or two diesel locomotives. The time to change traction, plus the lower permitted curving speeds of the diesel locomotives in Scotland would limit the time gain to be achieved, and there would be virtually no new market penetration.

Instead of sending the new trains north of Edinburgh to Aberdeen, they will from 1991 take advantage of the Carstairs-Edinburgh electrification. That scheme was originally proposed to promote through electric working of trains from Birmingham and other WCML locations to Edinburgh via Preston and Carlisle. However, it also makes possible the extension of King's Cross-Edinburgh trains each hour via Carstairs north curve to Motherwell and Glasgow. The market from Motherwell to Edinburgh by rail is a new one, and the linking of Glasgow to Newcastle and other points south on the ECML has already been shown to have potential. The previous IC125 service from King's Cross to Glasgow Queen Street will be withdrawn.

The capability to extend electrically-hauled IC225 trains to Glasgow Central comes from the decision not to have them working north to Aberdeen. Instead, Aberdeen is to be served by through diesel IC125 units from King's Cross. This provides additional capacity beyond that originally anticipated, to cater for traffic growth. Inverness will continue to have a daily IC125 from and to King's Cross.

Above right:
Trains which extend north of Edinburgh, or turn off to places like Hull, or which join the ECML from other routes such as the NorthEast-SouthWest, will continue to use diesel InterCity 125 sets. Thus the King's Cross-Aberdeen IC125s will still be seen crossing the Forth Bridge like this one on the 09.45 from Aberdeen on 4 March 1990. *Brian Morrison*

Right:
The now very common (indeed hourly) scene of a DVT leading an IC225 set out of Leeds virtually began with this launch special on 20 September 1989 which had power at the rear from No 90001 *Swallow*. *Brian Morrison*

Table 1

British Rail: Leeds-King's Cross; 7-3-90
Locomotive: Class 91 Bo-Bo electric No 91006
Load: 8 Mk 4 coaches + DVT; 346 tonnes tare; 360 tonnes gross

Dist miles		Scheduled min	Actual min sec	Speeds mph	Lateness min	Remarks
0.0	LEEDS	0	0 00	—	0	
			sigs	/44		
10.0	WAKEFIELD W.	11½	13 33	—	2	
0.0		0	0 00	—	5	4½min stop
1.7	Sandal		2 41	64		
	mp 172	[1½]	sigs	95 max		
		[2½]	pws	78 max		
19.9	DONCASTER	20	21 23	—	6	
0.0		0	0 00	—	5	1½min stop
2.8	Black Carr Junction	4	3 24		4½	
4.7	Rossington		4 25	111/115		
8.3	Bawtry	[2]	6 19	107/120/125		
17.4	RETFORD	15	12 21	—	2½	slow approach
0.0		0	0 00	—	3	1½min stop
				103/110/124		
18.5	NEWARK	13½	13 22	—	3	slow approach
0.0		0	0 00	—	4	2min stop
				115/123		
14.6	GRANTHAM	10½	10 01	—	3½	
0.0		0	0 00	—	4	2min stop
	High Dyke	[2]	4 00	93/101		
5.4	Stoke	7	4 50	116	2	
				124-126		
29.1	PETERBOROUGH	21	18 20	—	1½	slow approach
0.0		0	0 00	—	1	1½min stop
				104/111/122		
20.4	Offord		13 35	108		
24.7	St Neots		15 40	123-125		
32.3	Sandy	17	19 28	123-125	2	
35.3	Biggleswade	[3]	20 53	124-126		
44.5	HITCHIN		25 27	123		
49.8	Stevenage	28	27 31	125	½ early	
51.4	Knebworth		28 48	123		
56.1	Welwyn Garden City	32	30 34	pws	½ early	
58.7	HATFIELD		32 42	115		
63.7	Potter's Bar	36	35 21	115	½ early	
65.8	Hadley Wood	[2]	36 38	101/98		
67.2	New Barnet		37 33	97		
69.9	New Southgate		39 12	95		
71.4	Alexandra Palace	43	40 08		2 early	
	Hornsey		40 48	93		
			pws			
73.8	Finsbury Park	44½	41 55	60	1½ early	
76.4	KING'S CROSS	49*	46 26	—	1½ early*	

*Public timetable gives arrival time 3min later; train was 4½min early against the public time.
Figures in square brackets (eg [2]) are recovery times in minutes.

To see for myself how the new InterCity 225 trains perform in everyday running, I joined the 12.10 to King's Cross at Leeds on 7 March 1990. Locomotive No 91006 was at the rear, and the train was being driven from driving van trailer No 82207, with eight Mk 4s between that vehicle and the locomotive. Our 84ton Bo-Bo therefore had to shift a train totalling 430 tons tare, possibly 445 tons gross, including the weight of the locomotive. The run is logged in the Table.

Since the provision of digital clocks with second counters on station platforms, there has been a noticeable improvement in the accuracy of train starting times at many places. Our 12.10 was no exception, for my coach began to move at exactly 3sec after 12.10! The train was checked outside Wakefield Westgate, and there followed a station stop of 4½min, so we were 5min late away from there. Signals near milepost 172 brought us to a crawl. We recovered to a maximum of 95mph before a subsidence slack, and reached Doncaster after a brief acceleration to 78mph.

The 1½min station stop at Doncaster met the schedule so we were still 5min late. This gave added interest to the journey, to see how the new motive power responded to the challenge of time to be made up. Acceleration with a Class 91 is excellent, and we were up to 111mph by Rossington, 4.7 miles from the start! The maximum speed was 115 before slowing to around 107 at Bawtry. Maximum speed before the Retford stop was 125mph. The 17.4 miles took 12min 21sec, an average of 84.6mph start to stop.

Retford station stop was 1½min, and we left only 3min late, so time was being gained even on this short stretch. Retford to Newark, 18.5 miles, took 13min 22sec, an average of 83.1mph with a brief maximum of 124mph. The slow approach and 2min stop meant that the train left Newark 4min behind time. The 14.6 mile dash to Grantham took 10min 1sec, yet I clocked a maximum speed of 123mph near Barkston. That short run averaged 86.7mph, very creditable running, though Grantham was the only station stop I experienced on this trip which was not hampered by a slow approach to the platform.

From Grantham, also left 4min late, we accelerated up the 1 in 200 to 101mph as early as High Dyke and had reached 116mph by Stoke (5.4 miles). Down Stoke Bank we ran at a steady 124-126mph, indicating how accurately the locomotive's speed selection equipment holds the train speed to the '125' setting. Indeed, from the comfort of my seat in the train I was able for most of the rest of the journey to guess which speed setting had been selected by observing the speeds actually run! All were very close indeed to 5mph increments.

Peterborough was reached in 18min 20sec from Grantham, giving an average for that section of 95.3mph.

A 1½min station stop at Peterborough enabled us to start only a minute late on the final run to the capital. The comfort of the Mk 4 carriage (I have to admit) caused your observer brief periods when sleep would have been an attractive option! Suffice it to say that from St Neots to Knebworth we held speed closely between 123 and 126mph. Beyond the Welwyn tunnels we held speed rigidly to 115 to past Potter's Bar, and then to 95 until just north of Hornsey.

King's Cross was reached unchecked in 46min 26sec for the 76.4 miles. This averages at 98.7mph, lower than the magic 'ton' only because of the slower running necessary in the inner suburbs. Thus a 5min lateness from Doncaster had been converted into a 1½min early arrival at King's Cross (or 4½min early against the public timetable!), probably representing the best IC225 time achievable with full observance of present speed limits and approach control restrictions.

This run illustrates how difficult it is for an electric IC225 train to beat the best times already set up by diesel IC125 sets. However, although it is limited by the same maximum speed of 125mph, and with only 84 tons for adhesion compared with the 140 tons of

two IC125 powercars, a Class 91 can nonetheless put up a very creditable performance, particularly when considering its superb acceleration. With the line speed improvements now in place, and the predictability of Class 91 electronically-held speeds, we can expect to see further significant improvements in journey times and in timekeeping.

A major leap forward in journey times will come in the mid-1990s. InterCity aspires to take advantage of the 140mph design speed of the Class 91 and Mk 4 stock. Times for runs at this speed have not yet been set, but one can look forward to another major improvement, which will leave the West Coast route with a problem. How can the Euston-Glasgow run be brought down to less than the time it takes to get an IC225 from King's Cross to Edinburgh? Will the recently announced scheme to build InterCity 250 trains for the West Coast main line, with its hills and curves, enable WCML trains to beat the East Coast route to Scotland?

Or has East Coast main line supremacy already been established for all time?

Left:
On arrival at King's Cross on the run described in this chapter, passengers alight from the 12.10 from Leeds. The clock shows 14.40; the public timetable gives 14.42 as the arrival time of this train. The DVT has already been part emptied of its load of parcels. *Colin Boocock*

Below:
The sun glistens off new Mk 4 coaches and a DVT as the 11.10 from Leeds eases out of Platform 2 at Peterborough on 2 February 1990. *Dr W. A. Sharman*

Appendices

1. Traction and Rolling Stock

These photographs and diagrams portray the principal elements of an InterCity 225 train.

Right:
A Class 91 in repose: No 91006 rests at the rear of the 12.10 to King's Cross at Leeds on 7 March 1990. Both ends of the locomotive are fitted with standard BR buffing and drawgear as well as standard single phase electric train supply jumpers and standard air brake pipes. Push-pull control is through the train lighting wires, for which the jumpers are accessible through the covers in the sloping vehicle front. *Colin Boocock*

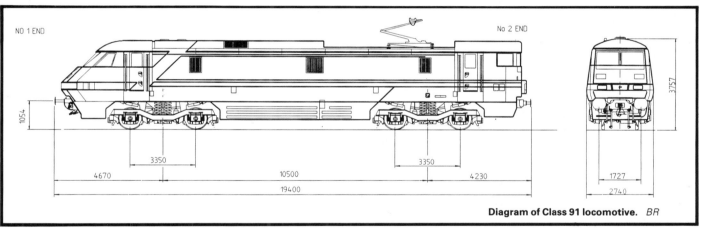

Diagram of Class 91 locomotive. *BR*

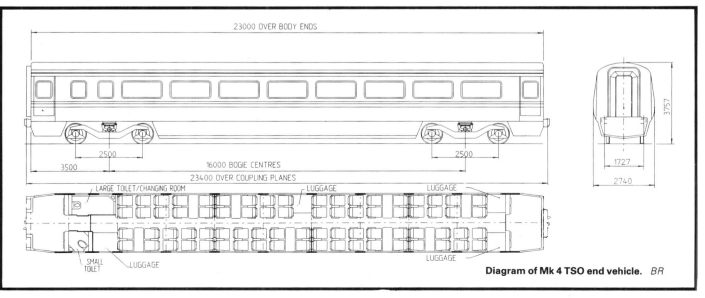

Diagram of Mk 4 TSO end vehicle. *BR*

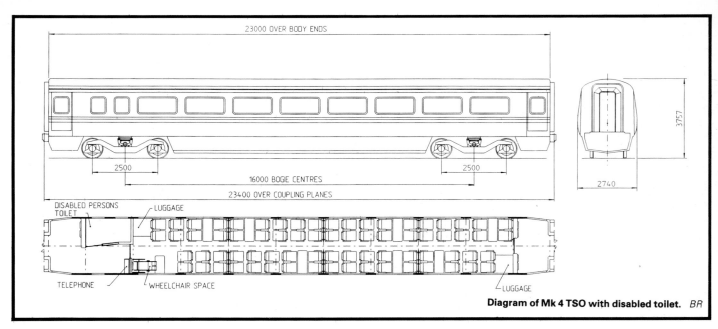

23000 OVER BODY ENDS

3757

2740

2500

2500

16000 BOGIE CENTRES

23400 OVER COUPLING PLANES

DISABLED PERSONS TOILET

LUGGAGE

TELEPHONE

WHEELCHAIR SPACE

LUGGAGE

Diagram of Mk 4 TSO with disabled toilet. *BR*

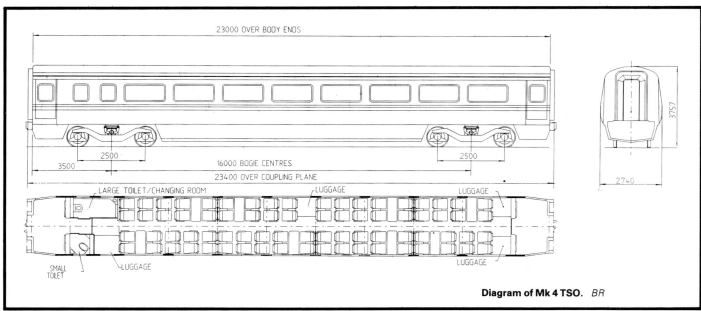

23000 OVER BODY ENDS

3757

2740

2500

2500

3500

16000 BOGIE CENTRES

23400 OVER COUPLING PLANE

LARGE TOILET/CHANGING ROOM

LUGGAGE

LUGGAGE

SMALL TOILET

LUGGAGE

LUGGAGE

Diagram of Mk 4 TSO. *BR*

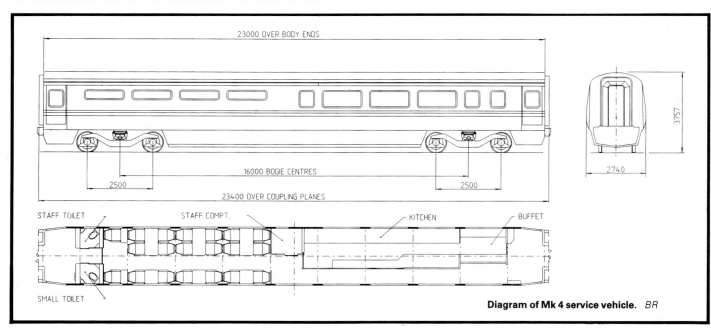

23000 OVER BODY ENDS

3757

2740

2500

2500

16000 BOGIE CENTRES

23400 OVER COUPLING PLANES

STAFF TOILET

STAFF COMPT.

KITCHEN

BUFFET

SMALL TOILET

Diagram of Mk 4 service vehicle. *BR*

Above:
Mk 4 coach No 11211, photographed at Wakefield Westgate on 7 March 1990 is a first class saloon vehicle. It uses the same bodyshell as a standard class coach. *Colin Boocock*

Above right:
This view of driving van trailer No 82206 at Leeds on 7 March 1990 shows the side doors giving access to the van interior. The guard's accommodation is at the rear of the vehicle.

The driving cab is fully streamlined to match the Class 91 cab profile at the other end of the train. *Colin Boocock*

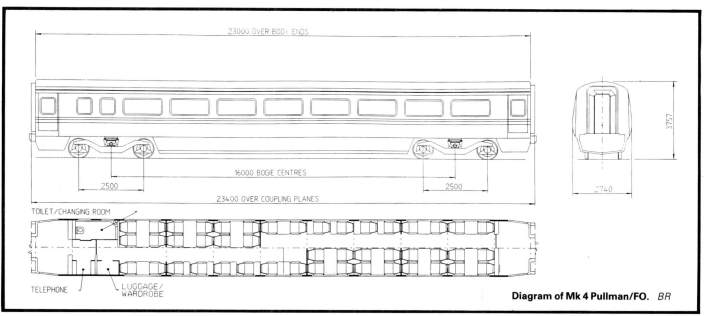

23000 OVER BODY ENDS

16000 BOGIE CENTRES

2500   2500

23400 OVER COUPLING PLANES

3757

2740

TOILET/CHANGING ROOM

TELEPHONE   LUGGAGE/WARDROBE

Diagram of Mk 4 Pullman/FO. *BR*

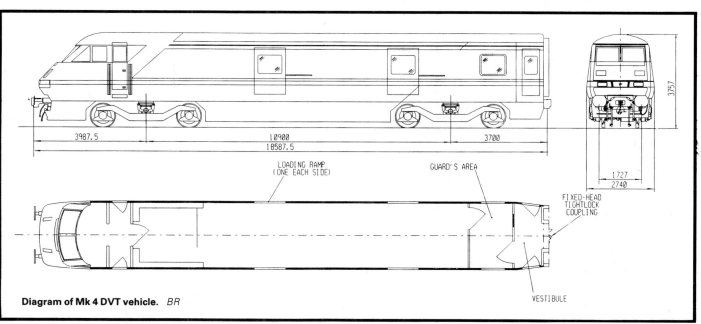

3987.5   10900   3700

18587.5

LOADING RAMP (ONE EACH SIDE)

GUARD'S AREA

FIXED-HEAD TIGHTLOCK COUPLING

VESTIBULE

3757

1727
2740

Diagram of Mk 4 DVT vehicle. *BR*

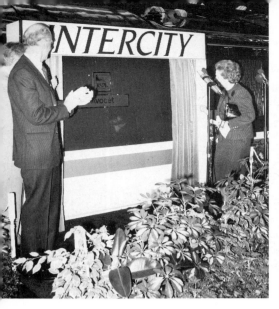

2. Ceremonies for Publicity

To keep the public aware of the investment going on in 'their' main line railway, British Rail's public affairs people staged many ceremonies which made the local or national newspapers or television networks. The photographs give a flavour of what was done.

Above left:
Locomotive-naming ceremonies are frequently used to bring public attention to notable events. The naming of the Brush Co-Co No 89001 *Avocet* **was carried out by the then Prime Minister, Mrs Margaret Thatcher at King's Cross on 16 January 1989. Looking on is Sir Robert Reid, Chairman of the British Railways Board, and Magnus Magnusson, President of the Royal Society for the Protection of Birds in recognition of which the locomotive was being named.** *Brian Morrison*

Above right:
Sir Robert was clearly pleased at the naming of the first Class 91 Bo-Bo *Swallow* **as GEC Chairman Lord Prior addresses the gathering at King's Cross on 20 September 1989.**
Brian Morrison

Right:
Up and down the ECML can be found electrification masts embellished with signs such as this one at Grantham station, where local interest in the electrification scheme was aroused by a mast-planting ceremony.
Colin Boocock

THIS MAST, THE 10,000TH ON THE EAST COAST MAIN LINE ELECTRIFICATION PROJECT, WAS "PLANTED" HERE AT GRANTHAM ON WEDNESDAY 15TH OCTOBER, 1986, BY THE RT. HON. JOHN MOORE, M.P., SECRETARY OF STATE FOR TRANSPORT.

Below left:
The ceremonial opening of the electrification construction depot at Millerhill near Edinburgh was a grand affair held on 13 April 1987. Lord Glenarthur and the ScotRail General Manager Jim Cornell (left) were raised on a mobile platform to unveil the depot sign. *Tom Noble*

Below:
At the same event, Lord Glenarthur is presented with a framed print of a Class 91 locomotive by ScotRail General Manager Jim Cornell. Below is a model of the former Glasgow & South Western Railway 4-4-0 *Lord Glenarthur.* *Tom Noble*